CW00855005

Contents

with special thanks to:

. . . . the children of Esher Church School
and Hinchley Wood First and Middle School
for learning and singing the songs with such enthusiasm
and for providing all the lovely illustrations

. . . . the staff for their kind co-operation and support

Printed by: Halstan & Co Ltd
               Plantation Road
               Amersham
               Bucks

Cover layout by: A R T Design
                  (037284) 2236

. . . . . and grateful thanks to God our creator whose excellence is our inspiration

A NOTE FROM THE AUTHORS

We are pleased to present *Songs For Every Season* - the first in a new series of music for Primary School children.

- In writing these songs we have included a wide variety of styles and in doing so we have sought to capture the mood and colour of the different seasons in a blend of words and music.

- Our aim has been to enrich and enlarge children's experience of music, language and of the world around them, whilst providing them with songs that they will enjoy singing.

- It is intended that *Songs For Every Season* be regarded not simply as a songbook or even just as a music resource. We believe that its potential lies in being used more creatively, in conjunction with other areas of the curriculum or even as a starting point for topic-based work.

- Lyric sheets have been included for you to photocopy or make into acetates. For copyright reasons we cannot allow you to photocopy the music or to copy the cassette.

- We do recommend that you use this book, together with the music cassette (OOTAM/002), and listen to the songs before you set out to teach them. We expect the backing-tracks to be helpful both as a teaching tool and in performance.

- We hope that you enjoy these new songs and would welcome any comments or suggestions you may have. Further copies of the music and/or cassette are available from the address at the back of the book.

Mark and Helen Johnson
February 1992

This edition reprinted April 1997

SONG FOR EVERY SEASON

CHORUS A   *There is a song for every season,*
Summer and Autumn, Winter, Spring.
Every new day you'll find a reason
To lift up your voice and sing.

CHORUS B   *There is a song in each day dawning,*
Wonderful sounds for us to hear.
Listen and you will hear them calling,
Whatever the time of year.

1   Whenever the sun is shining,
And when the days are nice and long,
With bags all packed to go on holiday,
I will sing a Summer song.

CHORUS A

2   Whenever the leaves are falling
And misty mornings chill the air,
I'll take a walk in my new wellies, and
I will sing an Autumn song.

CHORUS A

3   Whenever the wind is blowing,
And when the snow comes falling down,
From underneath my scarf and overcoat,
I will sing a Winter song.

CHORUS A

4   Whenever the birds are singing,
And when the day brings sudden showers,
I'll wait beneath my big umbrella, and
I will sing a Springtime song.

CHORUS A

5   So look at the seasons changing,
The world of nature turning round.
A year is like a big kaleidoscope,
Filled with colour, filled with sound.

CHORUS A & B

SONG FOR EVERY SEASON

Words & Music: Mark & Helen Johnson

Brightly ♩ = 140

There is a song for ev-'ry sea-son, Sum-mer and Aut-umn, Win-

ter, Spring. Ev'-ry new day you'll find a rea-son to

lift up your voice and sing. There is a song in each

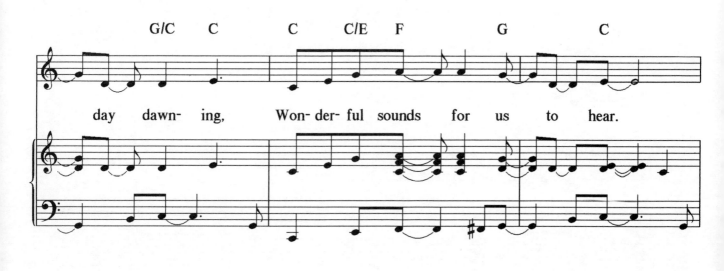

day dawn- ing,   Won- der- ful sounds   for   us   to   hear.

Last time to   Coda

Lis- ten and you   will   hear   them   call- ing,   What- ev- er the time   of   year.

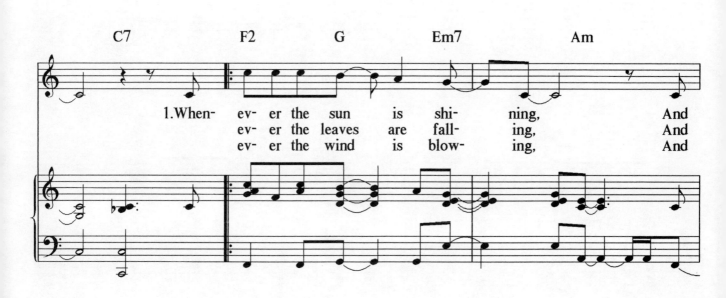

1.When- ev- er   the   sun   is   shi-   ning,   And
    ev- er   the   leaves   are   fall-   ing,   And
    ev- er   the   wind   is   blow-   ing,   And

6

4   Whenever the birds are singing,
    And when the day brings sudden showers,
    I'll wait beneath my big umbrella, and
    I will sing a Springtime song.

5   So look at the seasons changing,
    The world of nature turning round.
    A year is like a big kaleidoscope,
    Filled with colour, filled with sound.

8

CONKERS!

CHORUS *Conkers! . . . I'm collecting conkers,*
I'm trying hard to find the biggest and the best.
Conkers! . . . Lots of lovely conkers,
I want a conker that is better than the rest.

1   Under the chestnut tree,
There waits for me,
A sight so marv'llous to behold.
Amidst the Autumn leaves,
It gleams at me -
A conker, beautiful and bold.

CHORUS

2   Under the chestnut tree,
Where no-one's been,
The spiky shells lie on the ground.
Beneath their armour green,
There hides unseen,
A conker, smooth and shiny brown.

CHORUS

3   Under the chestnut tree,
I stretch to see,
A final conker to be mine.
If I can only reach
To pull it free,
I'll add it to my ninety-nine!

LAST CHORUS

Conkers! . . . I'm collecting conkers.
I'm trying hard to find the biggest and the best.
Conkers! . . . Lots of lovely conkers.
I think I've found that special one to beat the rest!

CONKERS!

Words & Music: Mark & Helen Johnson

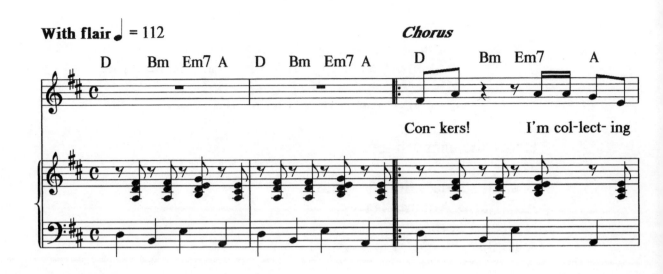

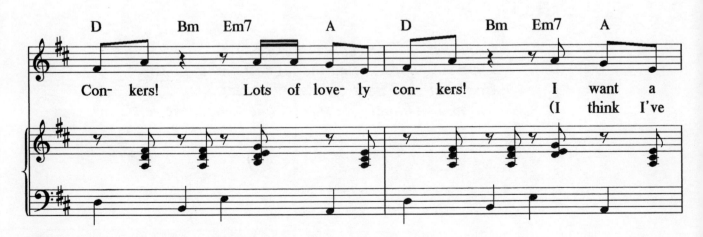

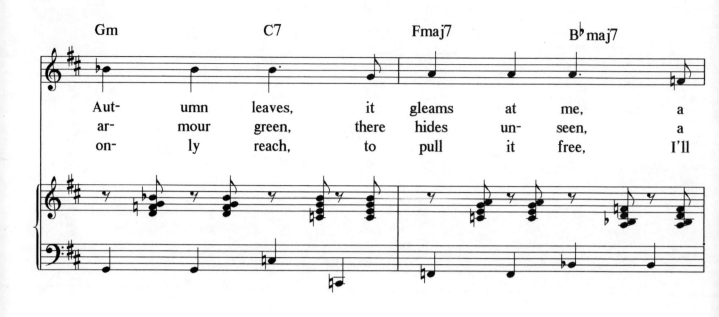

Gm   C7   Fmaj7   B♭maj7

Aut- umn leaves, it gleams at me, a
ar- mour green, there hides un- seen, a
on- ly reach, to pull it free, I'll

Gm   E7/G♯   Asus4   A

con- ker beaut- if- ul and bold.
con- ker, smooth and shi- ny brown,
add it to my nine- ty nine. (One hund- red!)

✪ **CODA**

D

rest!

12

HARVEST SONG

1   There is a farmer who stands in his fields,
     And he sees all the work to be done.
     He has been watching for many a month,
     He's been waiting for this time to come.

     CHORUS *There's a song to sing as the harvest comes in,*
     To the one who gives sunshine and rain.
     Let us all join in with a thank-offering,
     For the harvest that's gathered again.

2   There was a time when the fields were prepared,
     And the good soil was carefully ploughed.
     Then came the day for the farmer to sow,
     And the seeds were all scattered around.

     CHORUS

3   There was some time for the farmer to wait,
     As the seeds slowly grew out of sight.
     Then came the day when the first shoots appeared,
     And the farmer was filled with delight.

     CHORUS

4   Now is the time when the crops are full grown,
     And the farmer must gather them in.
     He'll need some help, 'cause there's lots to be done,
     And it's hard to know where to begin.

     CHORUS (x 2)

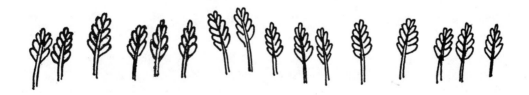

HARVEST SONG

Words & Music:Mark & Helen Johnson

wait- ing for this time to come.
seeds were all scat- tered a- round.
far- mer was filled with de- light. There's a
hard to know where to be- gin.

Chorus

song to sing as the har - vest comes in, to the One who gives sun- shine and

rain. Let us all join in with a thank - of- fer- ing for the

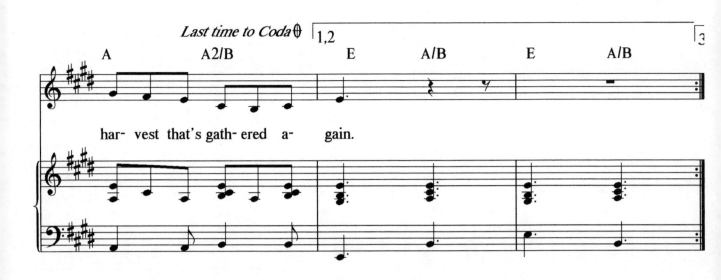

har- vest that's gath- ered a- gain.

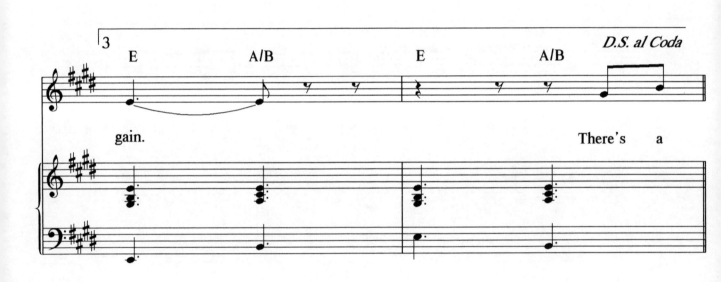

gain.   There's   a

gain.

TURN BACK THE CLOCKS

1   Turn back the clocks now that Harvest is over and done.
Look for the signs all around that the Autumn has come.

     CHORUS *The days are getting shorter,*
                       The nights are drawing in.
                       The air's getting much colder,
                       Now Autumn time has come again.

2   Look at the beautiful colours that blaze from the trees.
Orangy-red, green and yellows, so lovely to see.

     CHORUS

3   Sweep up the leaves that are falling all over the ground.
See all the squirrels go storing up nuts they have found.

     CHORUS

4   Soon there'll be grey misty mornings and fresh chilly air.
We'll wrap up warmly, but most of the trees will be bare.

     CHORUS

TURN BACK THE CLOCKS

Words & Music: Mark & Helen Johnson

1. Turn back the clocks now that Har- vest is ov- er and done. Look for the signs all ar- ound that the Aut- umn has come.
2. Look at the beaut- if- ul col- ours that blaze from the trees. Or- an- gy red, green and yell- ows so lov- ely to see.
3. Sweep up the leaves that are fall- ing all ov- er the ground. See all the squir- rels go stor- ing up nuts they have found.
4. Soon there'll be grey mis- ty mor- nings and fresh chil- ly air. We'll wrap up warm- ly but most of the trees will be bare.

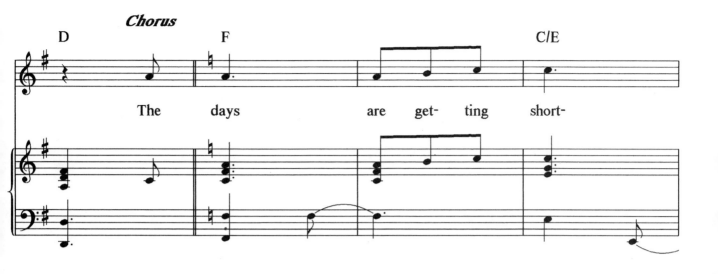

Chorus

The days are get- ting short-

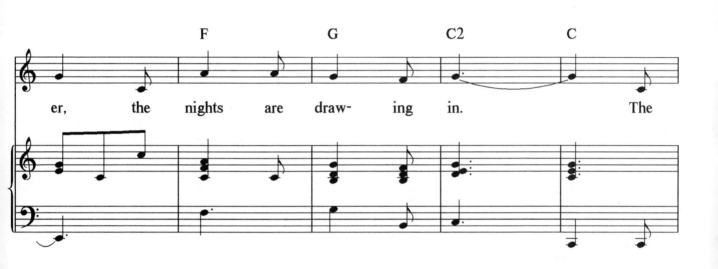

er, the nights are draw- ing in. The

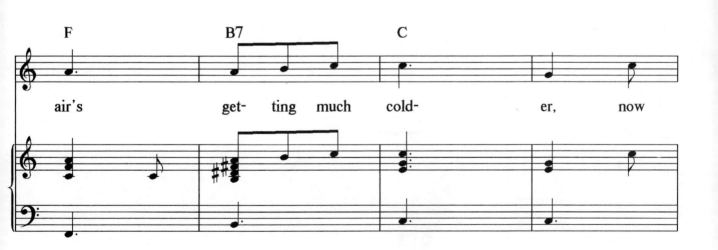

air's get- ting much cold- er, now

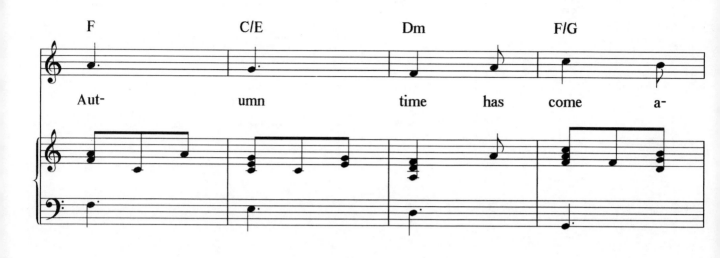

Aut- umn time has come a-

1,2,3

gain.

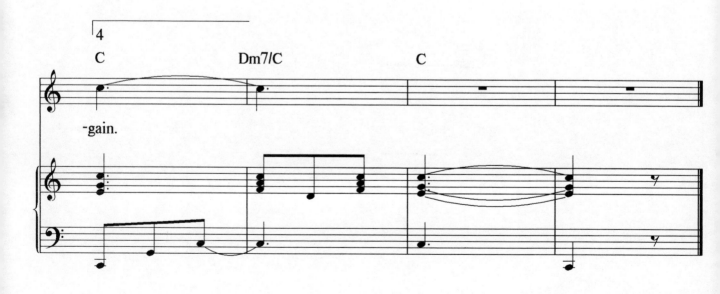

4

-gain.

WET PLAY

1   Did you hear the weather-man this morning,
Warning us about a cloudy day?
He said skies are getting grey and stormy,
Rainy weather now is on its way.

      CHORUS   *WET PLAY . . . . .*
                We can see, how it rains, and it pours,
                TO-DAY . . . . .
                We will stay, in the dry, keeping warm.
                WET PLAY . . . . .
                Can we paint? Can we read? Can we draw?
                TO-DAY . . . . .
                Can we write? Can we play, on the floor?

2   Dark clouds looming in the sky above me,
Look like they're about to burst with rain.
I'm quite happy sitting here all snugly,
Till the rainy weather goes away.

      CHORUS

3   There's a drizzle and a pitter-patter,
Raindrops tap against the window-pane.
I'm indoors, and so it doesn't matter,
How much rainy weather comes my way.

      CHORUS

4   Rain comes falling in a mighty downpour,
Rushing water floods the busy drains.
There's a splashing on the streets and sidewalks,
Looks like rainy weather's here to stay.

      CHORUS (x 2)

      <u>Last time</u> shout "WET PLAY!"

WET PLAY

Words & Music: Mark & Helen Johnson

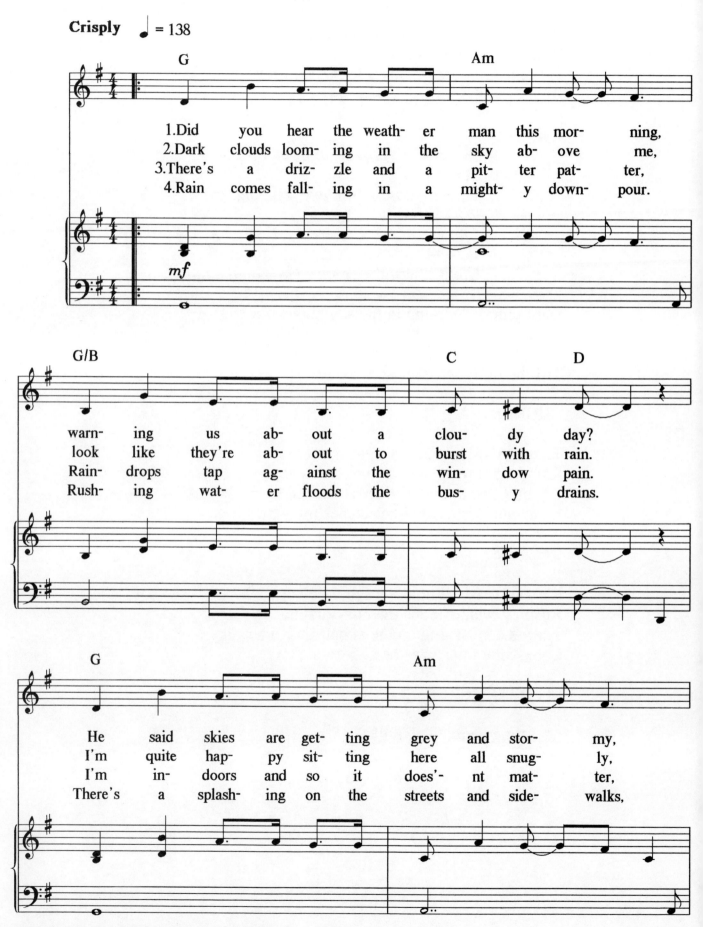

1.Did you hear the weath- er man this mor- ning,
2.Dark clouds loom- ing in the sky ab- ove me,
3.There's a driz- zle and a pit- ter pat- ter,
4.Rain comes fall- ing in a might- y down- pour.

warn- ing us ab- out a clou- dy day?
look like they're ab- out to burst with rain.
Rain- drops tap ag- ainst the win- dow pain.
Rush- ing wat- er floods the bus- y drains.

He said skies are get- ting grey and stor- my,
I'm quite hap- py sit- ting here all snug- ly,
I'm in- doors and so it does'- nt mat- ter,
There's a splash- ing on the streets and side- walks,

C · · · · · · · · · G

Can we paint? Can we read? Can we draw? TO- DAY, Can we write? Can we

| 1,2,3, | 4 |

D7 · · · · · · D7 · · · · · · *D.S. al Coda*

play on the floor? play on the floor? WET

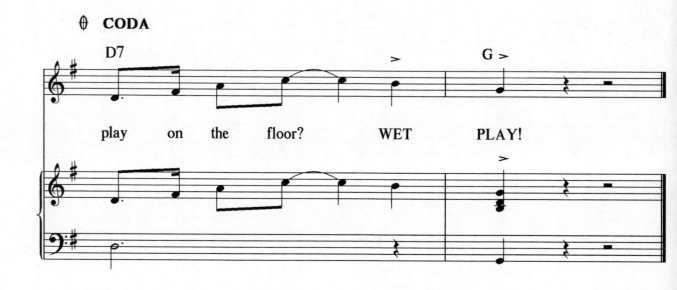

◉ **CODA**

D7 · · · · · · G >

play on the floor? WET PLAY!

SAD SONG
(In Winter)

1   Sad song in Winter,
     Plays a longing tune -
     For the life that has gone now,
     For colours that have faded from view.
     Skies bleak and grey now,
     Where they once were blue.
     And the ground, hard and frozen,
     Is hiding life that's going to break through.
          Winter is with us.
          The waiting has begun.
          Sad song remember -
          Spring will surely come.

2   Sad song in Winter,
     Plays a longing tune -
     For the birds that have flown now,
     For flowers that have fallen from bloom.
     Fields are so bare now,
     The scarecrow stands alone.
     Through the trees, sun shines softly,
     A promise of the life to come through.
          Winter is with us.
          The waiting has begun.
          Sad song remember -
          Spring will surely come.

SAD SONG

Words & Music: Mark & Helen Johnson

With feeling ♩ = 70

1.Sad song in Win - ter,
2.Sad song in Win - ter,

plays a long- ing tune,   for the life   that has
plays a long- ing tune,   for the birds,   that have

gone   now,   for col- ours that   have fad- ed from   view.
flown   now,   for flow- ers that   have fall- en from   bloom.

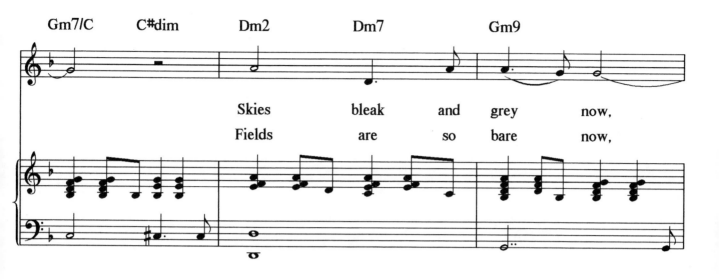

Skies bleak and grey now,
Fields are so bare now,

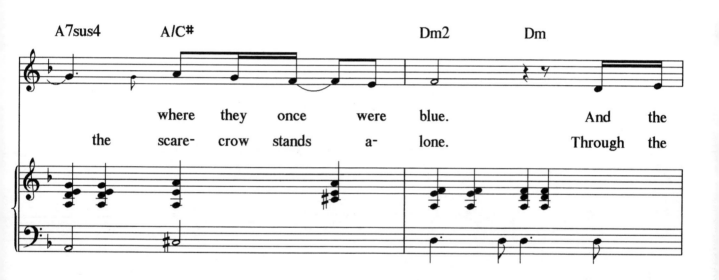

where they once were blue. And the
the scare- crow stands a- lone. Through the

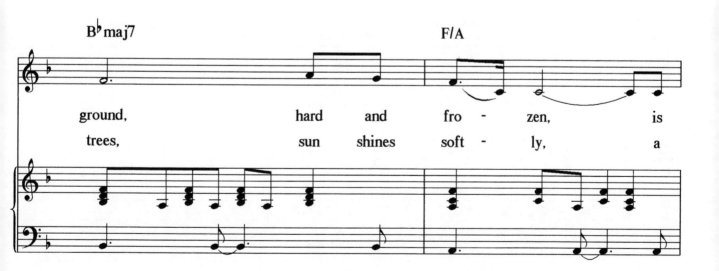

ground, hard and fro - zen, is
trees, sun shines soft - ly, a

hid- ing life that's going to break through.
prom- ise of the life to come through.

Chorus

Win- ter is with us,

The wait- ing has be- gun.

28

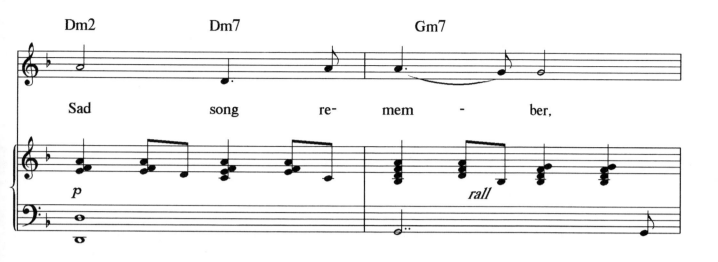

Sad song re- mem - ber,

Spring will sur- ely come.

come.

MERRY CHRISTMAS EVERYONE!

1   Christmas is near,
It's that time of year,
When we eat up lots of turkey and mince pies.
It's time for party hats,
And good cheer -
Merry Christmas ev'ryone!

CHORUS *When all the cards have been hung round the room,*
When the last decoration has been made.
And when you see Christmas lights on the trees,
Sing Happy Birthday to Jesus again.

2   Now is the time,
When the church-bells chime,
And the carol-singers stand out in the cold.
It's time for mistletoe,
Don't by shy -
Merry Christmas ev'ryone!

CHORUS

3   Christmas has come,
We're all having fun.
We've been making preparations for a while.
It's time to celebrate,
Sing along -
Merry Christmas ev'ryone!

CHORUS

LAST TIME CHORUS

Now all the cards have been hung round the room,
And the last decoration has been made.
Now we can see Christmas lights on the tree.
It's Happy Birthday to Jesus again!

MERRY CHRISTMAS EVERYONE

Words & Music: Mark & Helen Johnson

cheer, Mer- ry Christ- mas ev'- ry- one!
shy! Mer- ry Christ- mas ev'- ry- one!
long, Mer- ry Christ- mas ev'- ry- one!

𝄋 *Chorus*

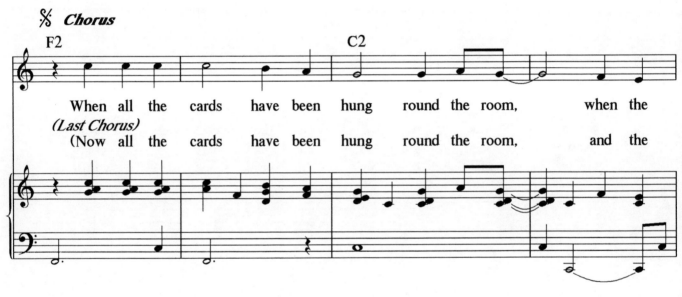

When all the cards have been hung round the room, when the
(Last Chorus)
(Now all the cards have been hung round the room, and the

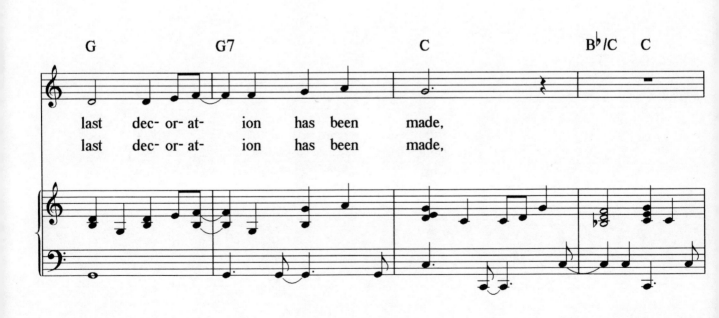

last dec- or- at- ion has been made,
last dec- or- at- ion has been made,

32

SNOW SONG
(Snow Is Falling Down)

1   Frosty weather casts a spell,
       On an unsuspecting world.
       Now the air has filled with magic,
       Snow is falling down.

2   Snow comes softly, drifting down,
       On the houses, all around.
       Over every street and rooftop,
       Snow is falling down.

       CHORUS: *Not a whisper, not a sound,*
               As snowflakes fall, and settle down.
               There's a hush, across the town,
               As snow comes falling down.

3   People tread through layers of snow,
       Leaving footprints as they go.
       Every step is leading homeward,
       Snow is falling down.

4   Cars are creeping slowly by,
       Window-wipers keeping time.
       Skies are full of winter weather,
       Snow is falling down.

       CHORUS

5   Wrapped in snowy eiderdown,
       Lies a quiet sleeping town.
       There is no-one there to notice,
       Snow is falling down.

       CHORUS

SNOW SONG

Words & Music:Mark & Helen Johnson

With a sense of wonder ♩ = 90

1.Fros- ty weath- er casts a spell, on an un- sus-
3.Peo- ple tread through layers of snow, leav- ing foot- prints

pect- ing world. Now the air has filled with mag- ic,
as they go. Ev'- ry step is lead- ing home- ward,

snow is fall- ing down.
snow is fall- ing down.

2.Snow comes soft- ly
4.Cars are creep- ing
5.Wrapped in sno- wy

37

SPRINGTIME

It's a beautiful day in springtime
It's a whistle a tune and sing time.
It's a breezy green grass and yellow dancing day.
It's a wonderful feeling.
Blossom and buds in bloom time.
It's a change-around, all things new time.
It's a happy hoppy healthy Springtime day.

SPRINGTIME

Words & Music: Mark & Helen Johnson

With bounce ♩ = 138

It's a beaut- if- ul day in Spring- time, it's a

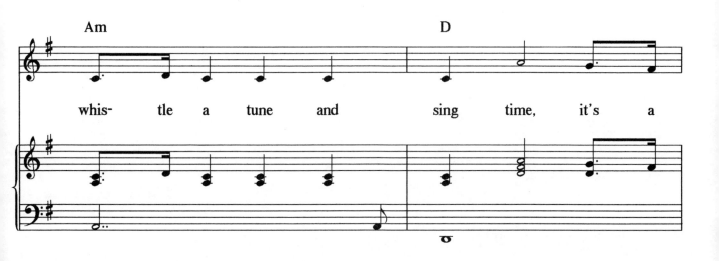

whis- tle a tune and sing time, it's a

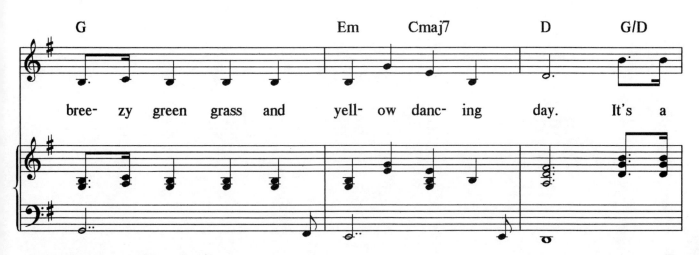

bree- zy green grass and yell- ow danc- ing day. It's a

won- der -ful feel- ing. Bloss- om and buds in bloom time, It's a

change a- round all things new time. It's a hap- py, hop- py,

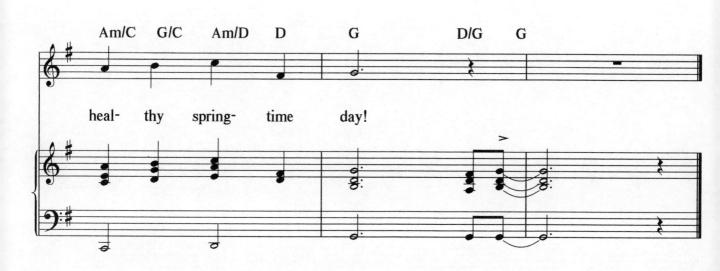

heal- thy spring- time day!

PANCAKES!

1 It's Shrove Tuesday, Pancake Day has come.
  Time for some cooking, time for having fun.
  We'll make some pancakes, lots for everyone.
  It's Shrove Tuesday, Pancake Day has come.

2 Making pancakes needs a careful plan,
  Eggs, milk and flour, butter and a pan.
  "Better roll your sleeves up, better wash your hands".
  Making pancakes needs a careful plan.

3 For the mixture, this is what you do -
  Blend the ingredients with a wooden spoon.
  Stir it round in circles, 'til it's nice and smooth.
  For the mixture, this is what you do.

4 Heat some butter, in a frying pan.
  Pour in the batter, cook it golden brown.
  Give the pan a jiggle, shake it all around.
  Now toss the pancake . . . . catch it if you can.
  Now toss the pancake . . . . catch it if you can!

PANCAKES

Words & Music: Mark & Helen Johnson

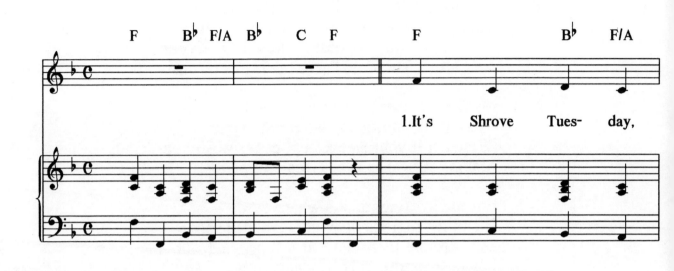

1. It's Shrove Tues- day,

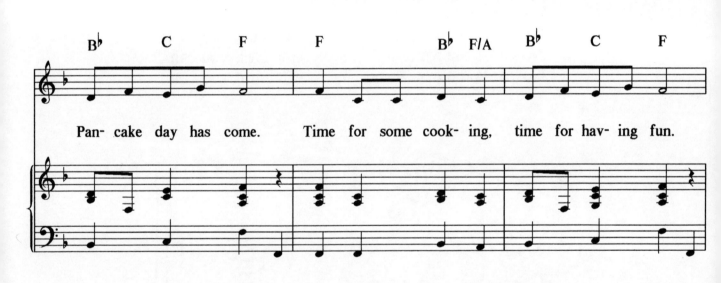

Pan- cake day has come. Time for some cook- ing, time for hav- ing fun.

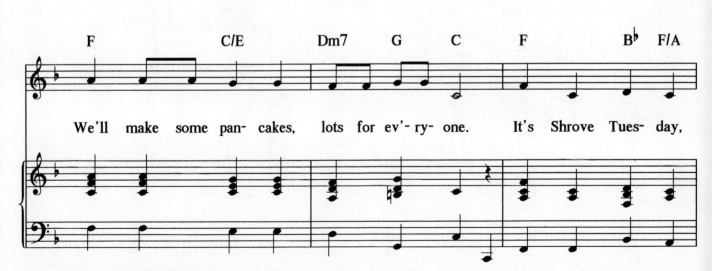

We'll make some pan- cakes, lots for ev'- ry- one. It's Shrove Tues- day,

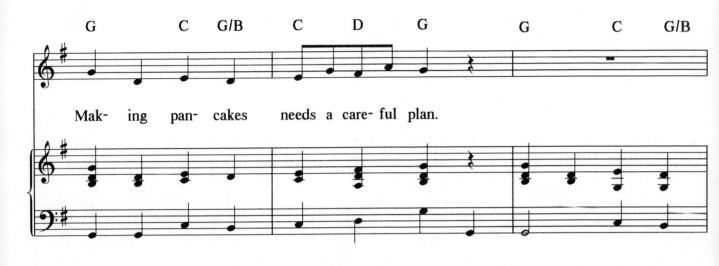

Mak- ing pan- cakes needs a care- ful plan.

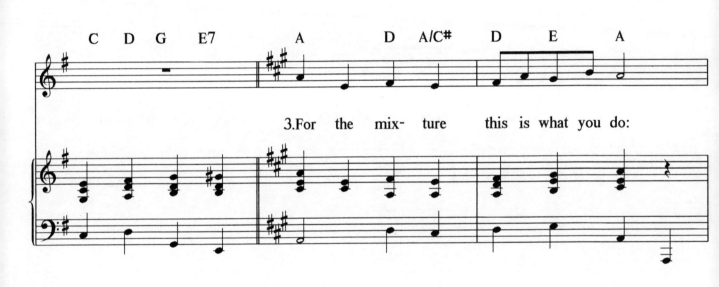

3.For the mix- ture this is what you do:

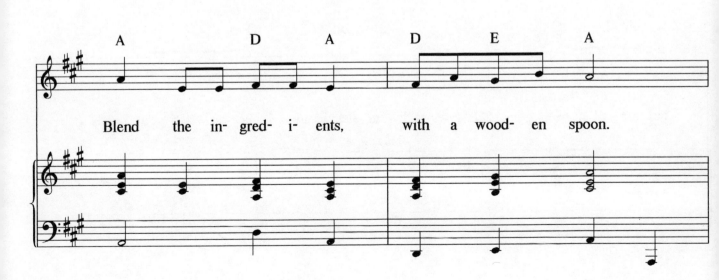

Blend the in- gred- i- ents, with a wood- en spoon.

Stir it round in cir- cles, 'til it's nice and smooth. For the mix- ture,

this is what you do.

4. Heat some butt- er in a fry- ing pan. Pour in the bat- ter

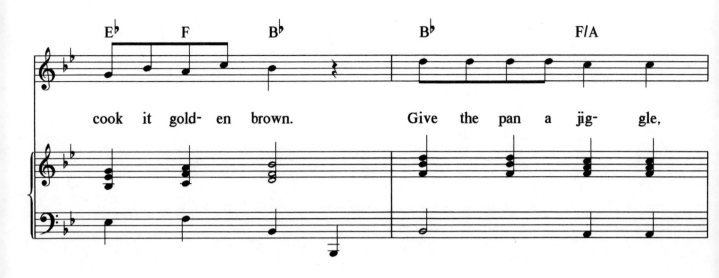

cook it gold- en brown. Give the pan a jig- gle,

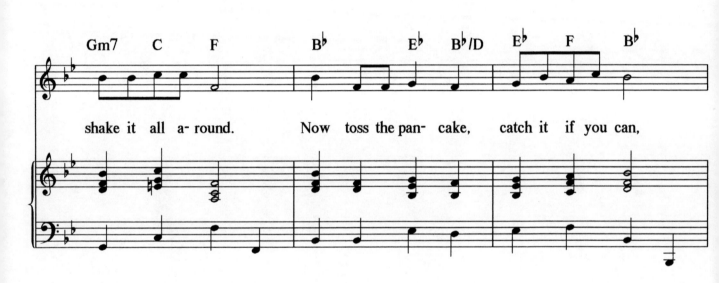

shake it all a- round. Now toss the pan- cake, catch it if you can,

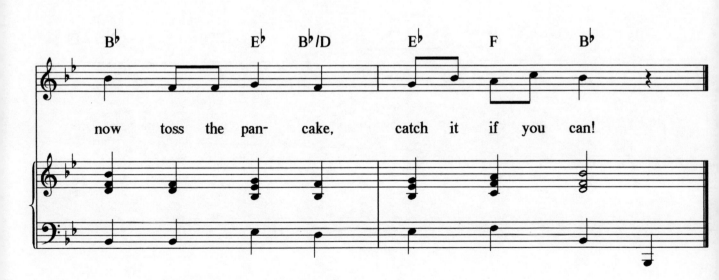

now toss the pan- cake, catch it if you can!

SING OUT AN EASTER SONG

CHORUS *Sing out an Easter song,*
Tell ev'ryone that the Lord has risen.
Sing out a joyful song,
Tell ev'rybody that He's alive!

1 Jesus Christ, Son of God,
Gave His life, upon a cross.
But the power of death was not
Enough to hold Him down.

CHORUS

2 Taken down, from public view,
He was placed inside a tomb.
But the power of Love broke through,
And raised Him back to life!

CHORUS

3 He returned, to see His friends,
Showed Himself alive again.
What a day it must have been
To have Him back again!

CHORUS (x 2)

SING OUT AN EASTER SONG

Words & Music: Mark & Helen Johnson

With enthusiasm ♩ = 170

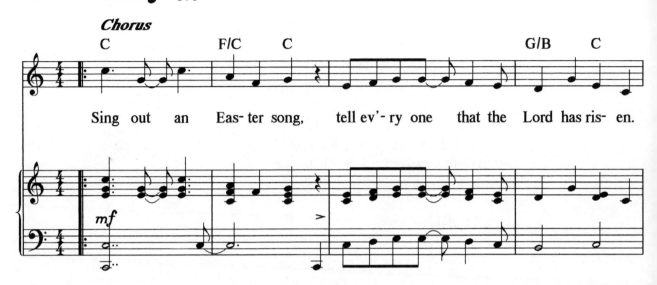

Sing out an Eas-ter song, tell ev'-ry one that the Lord has ris-en.

Sing out a joy-ful song, Tell ev'-ry-bo-dy that He's a-live!

Last time to Coda

N.B. Repeat Chorus after v.3

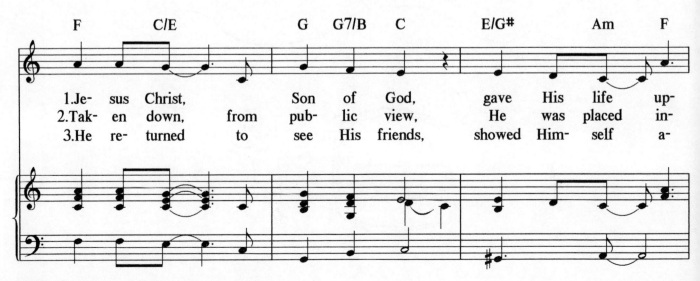

1. Je-sus Christ, Son of God, gave His life up-
2. Tak-en down, from pub-lic view, He was placed in-
3. He re-turned to see His friends, showed Him-self a-

MAYTIME

1   May-time has started
     Come and party in the sun.
     Dance round the maypole,
     Show the people, how it's done.
          Weave all the coloured ribbons in and out,
          You'll be having some fun!
     May-time has started
     Come and party in the sun.

2   All round the nation
     Celebrations have begun.
     Join in the laughter,
     Find a partner, everyone.
          Skip to the rhythm of the dancing song,
          You'll be singing along!
     All round the nation
     Celebrations have begun.

3   INSTRUMENTAL VERSE

4   May-time has started
     Come and party in the sun.
     Dance round the maypole,
     Show the people, how it's done.
          Weave all the coloured ribbons in and out,
          You'll be having some fun!
     May-time has started
     Come and party in the sun.

MAYTIME

Words & Music: Mark & Helen Johnson

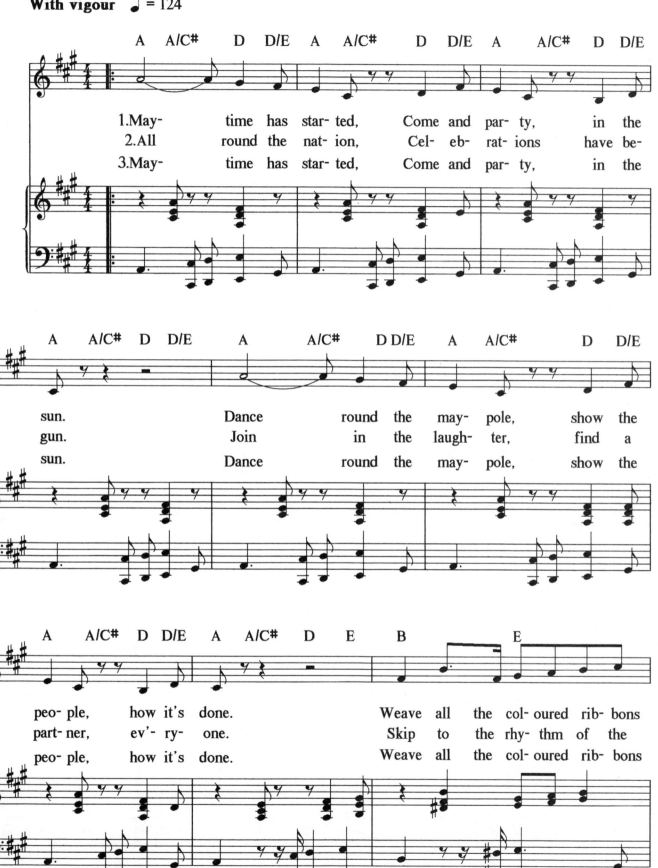

NOW THAT SUMMER HAS COME

1   The sun's in the sky,
      The temperature's rising.
      The clouds have gone by,
      The outlook is fine - and so am I!
      This lovely weather,
      Has got me singing a happy tune.
      All my cares have gone, now that summer has come.

2   The birds in the trees,
      Are whistling sweetly.
      The delicate breeze,
      Is keeping me cool, and feeling fine.
      This lovely weather,
      Has got me singing a happy tune.
      All my cares have gone, now that summer has come.

3   The sun's in the sky,
      The temperature's rising.
      The clouds have gone by,
      The outlook is fine - and so am I!
      This lovely weather,
      Has got me singing a happy tune.
      All my cares have gone, now that summer has come.

NOW THAT SUMMER HAS COME

Words & Music:Mark & Helen Johnson

Breezily ♩ = 138

1.The sun's in the sky. The temp- 'ra- ture's
2.The birds in the trees, Are whist- l- ing

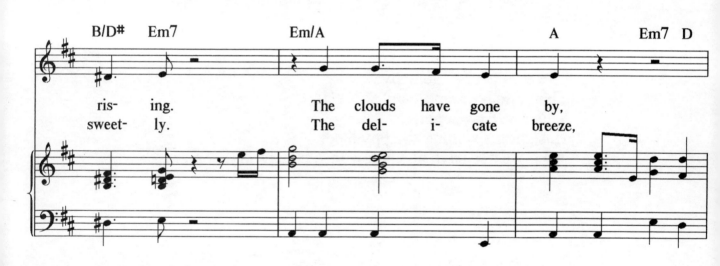

ris- ing. The clouds have gone by,
sweet- ly. The del- i- cate breeze,

The out- look is fine, and so am I. This love- ly
Is keep- ing me cool, and feel- ing fine. This love- ly

weath- er,   has got me sing- ing a hap- py tune.
weath- er,   has got me sing- ing a hap- py tune.

All my cares have gone, now that sum- mer has come.
All my cares have gone, now that sum- mer has come.

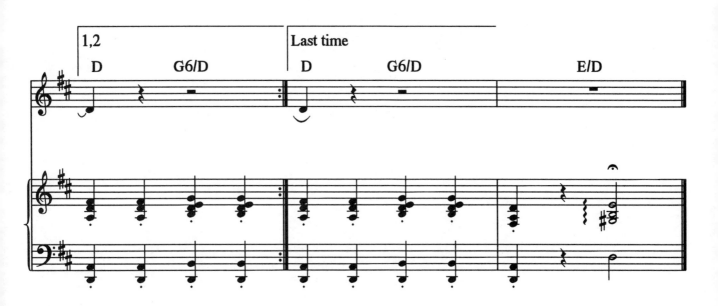

LOVELY SUMMER'S DAY

1   Say Hello to Summer,
Wave Goodbye to Spring.
Take a look at what the season brings.
   There's so much that I could say,
   On this lovely Summer's day.

2   Smell the lovely roses,
Feel the beaming sun.
Listen to the blackbird sing its song.
   There's so much that I could say,
   On this lovely Summer's day.

3   Bumble bees are busy,
Buzzing as they go.
Butterflies are flitting to and fro.
   There's so much that I could say,
   On this lovely Summer's day.

4   Skies are blue and silent,
Aeroplanes fly high,
Making chalky lines across the sky.
   There's so much that I could say,
   On this lovely Summer's day.

5   Say Hello to Summer,
Wave Goodbye to Spring.
Take a look at what the season brings.
   There's so much that I could say,
   On this lovely Summer's day.

LOVELY SUMMER'S DAY

Words & Music: Mark & Helen Johnson

Light and jolly ♩ = 102

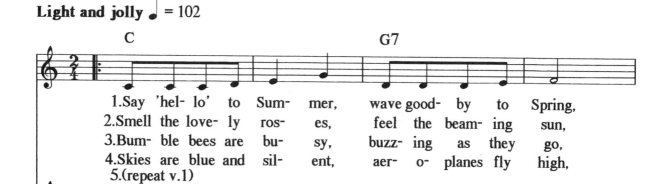

1. Say 'hel-lo' to Sum-mer, wave good-by to Spring,
2. Smell the love-ly ros-es, feel the beam-ing sun,
3. Bum-ble bees are bu-sy, buzz-ing as they go,
4. Skies are blue and sil-ent, aer-o-planes fly high,
5. (repeat v.1)

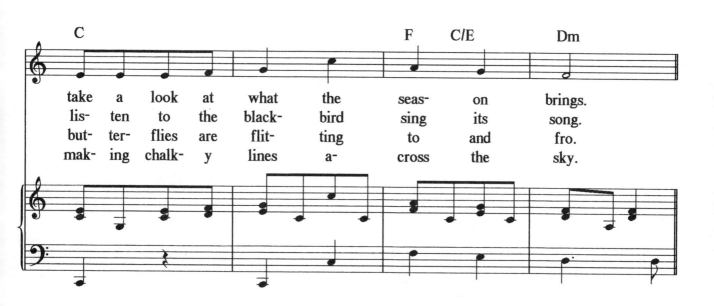

take a look at what the seas-son brings.
lis-ten to the black-bird sing its song.
but-ter-flies are flit-ting to and fro.
mak-ing chalk-y lines a-cross the sky.

Chorus

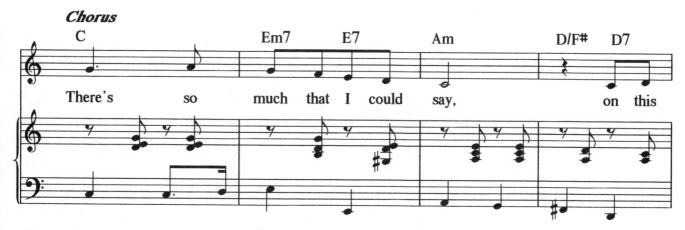

There's so much that I could say, on this

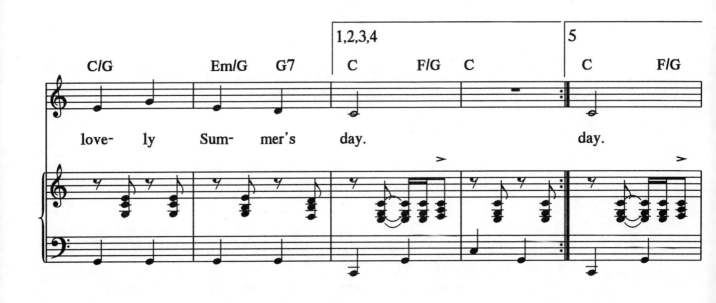

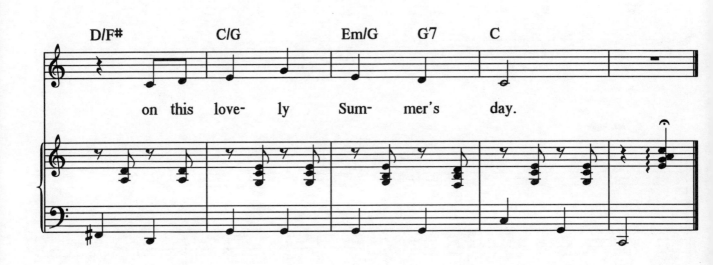

LAZY DAYS
(Dreaming)

1   Lazy days and summer sunshine,
What a way to spend my time.
Playing games and having fun times,
In the shade and feeling fine.

             CHORUS   *Dreaming . . . . of going on a holiday*
With sun and sea,
To places that I've never been before,
Out of doors,
Doin' all the things I've always wanted to.
I'll see the sights,
I'll hit the heights,
Then I'll have a lazy afternoon.

2   Making plans to build a castle,
In the sand, for all to see.
Looking at the water sparkle,
Sitting back, with my ice-cream.

      CHORUS

3   Taking walks on empty beaches,
Thinking thoughts of lovely things.
Listen for the seagull screeches,
On the shore, the waves come in.

             CHORUS   *Dreaming . . . . of going on a holiday*
With sun and sea,
To places that I've never been before,
Out of doors.
Doin' all the things I've always wanted to.
I'll see the sights,
I'll hit the heights,
Then I'll have a lazy afternoon . . .
Then I'll have a lazy afternoon . . . . . . (Aaaahh!)

LAZY DAYS

Words & Music: Mark & Helen Johnson

With a light jazz swing ♩ = 120

1. La-zy days and sum-mer sun-shine, what a way to
2. Mak-ing plans, to build a cas-tle in the sand, for
3. Tak-ing walks, on emp-ty bea-ches, think-ing thoughts of

spend my time! Play-ing games and hav-ing fun times,
all to see. Look-ing at the wa-ter spar-kle,
love-ly things. Lis-ten for the sea-gull scree-ches.

Chorus

in the shade, and feel-ing fine.
sit-ting back with my ice-cream. Dream-ing of
On the shore, the waves come in.

go- ing on a hol- i- day with sun and sea, to

pla- ces that I've nev- er been be- fore, out of doors.

Do- in' all the things I've al- ways wan- ted to. I'll see the

sights,   I'll   hit   the   heights,   then   I'll   have   a   la-   zy   af- ter-

1,2   **3**

noon.   noon,

then   I'll   have   a   la-   zy   af- ter-   noon.   Aaaahh!